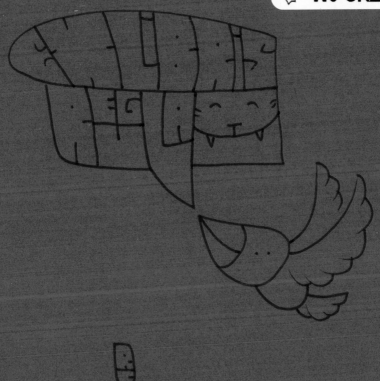

TeN COUNTiNG CaT

library edition

by ROBERT CHAPLiN *rca bfa*

© AD MMV The Publisher
P.O. Box# 123 Telkwa
British Columbia VOJ 2XO

iSBN 1-894897-34-X

COPY CaTS aRE DiRTY RaTS

CHAPLiN, ROBERT.   TEN COUNTiNG CAT.   iLLUS. by ROBERT CHAPLiN.
SUMMARY: DEFiNiTiVE COUNTiNG BOOK, FOLLOWS THE LiFE OF A CAT
COUNTiNG BiRDS TO NiNE. CONCLUDES WiTH TABLES WHiCH EXPLAiN
COUNTiNG THEORY, SCiENTiFiC NOTATiON, THE HiSTORY AND THE TAX-
ONOMY OF REALLY BiG NUMBERS, iNCLUDiNG THE GOOGOLPLEX AND
iNFiNiTY

1. CATS - COUNTiNG   1. TiTLE

iSBN: 1-894897-OO-5,   1-894897-18-8 (infinity ed.),
1-894897-34-X (Library ed.)

PRiNTED iN CANADA

THIS BOOK WAS DESIGNED AT GOGGLEBOX
TYPESET IN HIGH FUNK PALATINO
PRINTED ON ACID FREE PAPER
AND BOUND WITH LOVE

WORDS OF GRATITUDE TO THOSE WHO CAME BEFORE
AND TO THOSE WHO HELPED, THIS BOOK IS

DEDICATED

TO THE MEMORY OF MY GRANDPARENTS
GILBERT, JEAN, LAURA, & CHARLIE

1 CAT IS HAPPY

1 BIRD IS DEAD

2

BiRD iS FLYiNG OVERHEAD

CAT HAS TWO BiRDS

THEY ARE DEAD

3 BiRD iS
SiNGiNG
CaT HeaRS
SoUND

THRee DeaD BiRDS
LaY oN THe GRoUND

CAT IS
JOLLY
KEEPING
SCORE
COUNT DEAD BIRDIES
THERE ARE

FOUR 4

BiRD
iN SKY iS
STiLL
aLiVe

CaT iS CHeeRFUL

DeaD
BiRDS
FiVe

6 SiX DeaD BiRDS aND CaT FeeLS GREaT

$$\frac{\begin{array}{r} 7 \\ +1 \end{array}}{8}$$

SeVeN DeaD BiRDS PLUS oNe

MaKes eiGHT

9 NiNe BiRDie CORPSeS

CaT

FeeLS

TiReD

BUGS aRe HaPPY

CaT'S
eXPiReD

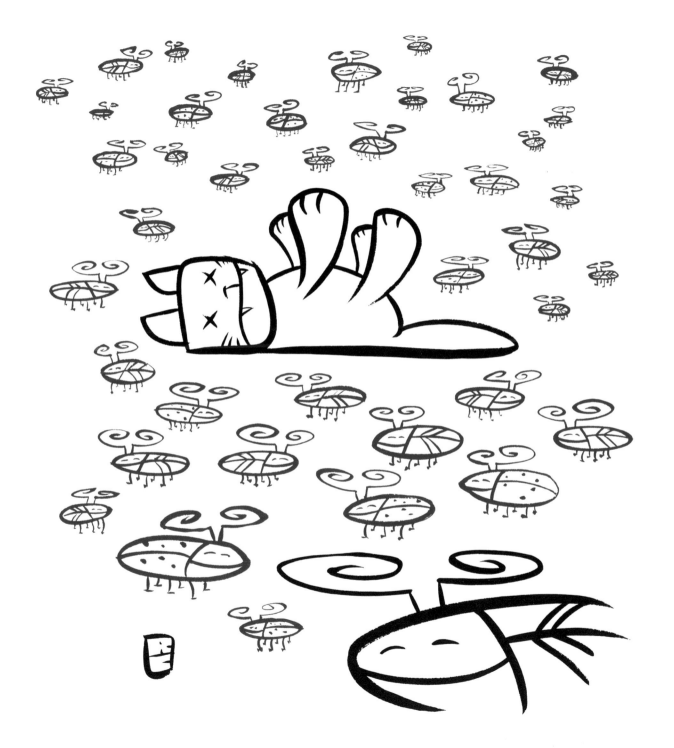

TeN iS aFTeR NiNe

MORE COUNTiNG FOR COUNTiNG PAST TEN

10

11,12,13,14
15,16,17,18,19
2O,21,22,23,24
25,26,27,28,29

3O,4O,5O,6O,7O,8O,9O

1OO..HUNDREDS
1,OOO.................................THOUSANDS
1O,OOO.......................TEN THOUSANDS
1OO,OOO........HUNDRED THOUSANDS
1,OOO,OOO................................MiLLiONS
1O,OOO,OOO..................TEN MiLLiONS
1OO,OOO,OOO...HUNDRED MiLLiONS
1,OOO,OOO,OOO...............BiLLiONS ✳

iNFiNiTY iS WAY AFTER TEN

...

FOR COUNTiNG REALLY BiG NUMBERS WE MAY USE SCiENTiFiC NOTATiON THE LiTTLE NUMBERS iN SUPER SCRiPT ARE CALLED EXPONENTS AND THEY REPRESENT THE NUMBER OF MULTiPLiCATiONS

IN THiS FORM, ONE THOUSAND iS REPRESENTED AS 10^3 WHiCH iS, TEN TO THE POWER OF THREE, OR

$$10x10x10$$

TEN THOUSAND iS, TEN TO THE POWER OF FOUR $10^4 = 10x10x10x10$ A HUNDRED THOUSAND iS TEN TO THE POWER OF FiVE $10^5 = 10x10x10x10x10$ ONE MiLLiON IS TEN TO THE POWER OF SiX $10^6 = 10x10x10x10x10x10$

*END NOTES

THERE SEEMS TO BE SOME DISCREPANCY AMONG ARITHMETICIANS REGARDING THE ASSIGN-MENT OF NAMES TO REALLY REALLY BIG NUMBERS.

IN THE 15th CENTURY, NICHOLAS CHUQUET MADE UP THE NAMES FOR COUNTING BIG NUMBERS, BILLION TRILLION, QUADRILLION QUINTILLION, SEXTILLION SEPTILLION OCTILLION, & NONILLION. BY CHUQUET'S COUNTING, ONE BILLION IS EQUAL TO ONE MILLION MILLIONS. THIS SYSTEM IS STILL IN USE IN THE UNITED KINGDOM.

IN THE 17th CENTURY FRENCH EXPERTS BEGAN TO USE THE SAME WORDS TO COUNT DIFFERENTLY. BY THE FRENCH SYSTEM ONE BILLION WOULD BE EQUAL TO ONE THOUSAND MILLIONS. THIS SYSTEM IS CURRENTLY FAVOURED IN NORTH AMERICA

COUNTiNG BiGGER THAN ONE MiLLiON

	CAN	UK
MiLLiARD		10^9
BiLLiON	10^9	10^{12}
TRiLLiON	10^{12}	10^{18}
QUADRiLLiON	10^{15}	10^{24}
QUiNTiLLiON	10^{18}	10^{30}
SEXTiLLiON	10^{21}	10^{36}
SEPTiLLiON	10^{24}	10^{42}
OCTiLLiON	10^{27}	10^{48}
NONiLLiON	10^{30}	10^{54}

GOOGOL

iS TEN TO THE POWER OF ONE HUNDRED..... 10^{100}

GOOGOLPLEX

iS TEN TO THE POWER OF GOOGOL, A VERY BiG NUMBER iNDEED............ $10^{\left(10^{100}\right)}$

∞ iNFiNiTY

iS EVEN BiGGER THAN A GOOGOLPLEX TO THE POWER OF GOOGOLPLEX. AND ONE OVER iNFiNiTY iS SMALLER THAN YOU CAN EVEN iMAGiNE.

AND THEN SOME ... $\dfrac{1}{\infty}$